Si-sa-yong-o-sa, Inc.
55-1, Chongno 2-ga, Chongno-gu
Seoul 110, Korea

Si-sa-yong-o-sa, Inc., New York Office
115 West 29th Street, 5th Floor
New York, NY 10001
Tel : (212) 736-5092

Si-sa-yong-o-sa, Inc., Los Angeles Office
3053 West Olympic Blvd., Suite 208
Los Angeles, California 90006
Tel : (213) 387-7105/7106

ISBN 0-87296-013-7

Printed in Korea

The Spring of Youth
젊어지는 샘물
Three-Year Hill
3년 고개

Adapted by Mark C. K. Setton
Illustrated by Lee Han-joong

Si-sa-yong-o-sa, Inc.
Seoul • New York • Los Angeles

The Spring of Youth

This is the story of an old man and an old woman who lived deep in the mountains a very long time ago. They led a poor, simple life, and they had to work very hard just to stay alive.

Every morning the old man would go into the mountains to chop wood, and then he would sell it down in the valley. It was heavy work for a feeble old man to do, but all the same he did it day in and day out without complaining. He even wished that he were young and strong enough to do more work.

Everyone in the neighborhood felt sorry that such kind and gentle old folk had to lead such a hard life, and especially that they had no children.

젊어지는 샘물

이 이야기는 먼 옛날 깊은 산속에 살고 있던 어느 할아버지와 할머니의 이야기입니다. 할아버지와 할머니는 가난하고 소박하게 살았으며, 목숨을 부지하기 위해서 부지런히 일을 해야만 했읍니다.

할아버지는 아침마다 산속으로 들어가서 나무를 해다가 골짜기 아랫 마을로 나무를 팔러 가곤 했읍니다. 기력이 없는 할아버지에게는 힘드는 일이었지만, 날이면 날마다 불평하지 않고 한결같이 그 일을 했읍니다. 할아버지는 일을 좀더 많이 할 수 있도록 좀더 젊고 힘이 세었으면 좋겠다고 생각했읍니다.

이웃사람들은 모두 그처럼 착하고 너그러운 노인네들이 이렇게 힘들게 살아가는 데다, 자식도 없기 때문에 안타깝게 생각했읍니다.

There was another lonely old man, a farmer, who lived nearby. He had no children either, and to make matters worse, his wife had died many years before, leaving him all alone.

But nobody felt sorry for him, as he was a crafty old fellow who made a living by cheating other people and lying. In fact, everybody hated him except the old man and woman, who were too kind-hearted to hate anyone.

One morning the kind old man went up into the mountains to work as usual. But on that day, something very unusual happened. He had been chopping away for some time and was feeling quite hot and tired.

At that moment, a little bird flew down from the sky and settled on a branch high above the old man's head. Then it started to sing the most beautiful song he had ever heard in all his years. The whole forest fell silent at the sound of the bird's voice.

4

이웃에는 또다른 할아버지 농부 한 사람이 외롭게 살고 있었읍니다. 그 할아버지에게도 자식이 없었는데 설상가상으로 그의 아내가 할아버지 혼자만 남겨둔 채 오래 전에 이 세상을 떠나 버렸읍니다.

그러나 그 할아버지는 남을 속이고 거짓말하면서 살아가는 간사한 할아버지였으므로 아무도 그를 불쌍하게 생각하지 않았읍니다. 사실은 마음씨가 너무 착해서 아무도 미워하지 않는 그 할아버지와 할머니 외에는 모두들 그를 미워했읍니다.

어느 날 아침에 그 친절한 할아버지는 여느 때처럼 일을 하러 산으로 갔읍니다. 그러나 그날은 아주 이상한 일이 일어났읍니다. 할아버지는 한참 동안 나무를 찍다가 매우 덥고 피곤함을 느꼈읍니다.

바로 그때 작은 새 한 마리가 하늘에서 날아와선 할아버지의 머리 위에 있는 높은 나뭇가지에 내려 앉았읍니다. 그리고는 할아버지가 난생 처음 들어보는 가장 아름다운 노래를 하기 시작했읍니다. 새의 노래소리에 온 숲속은 쥐죽은 듯 조용해졌읍니다.

The old man dropped his axe and sat down to listen as if he were under a spell. As he listened, all his worries seemed to melt away. He could think of nothing but the sweet sound of the little bird's song.

Suddenly the bird flew off and settled on another tree further up the mountain. Then it started to sing its entrancing song again. The old man got up and walked towards the sound of the bird.

As soon as he drew near though, it flew off and settled on another branch further away. The old man didn't want to lose the bird at any cost, so he hurried after it again.

In this way the little bird led him deeper and deeper into the forest. At last it came to rest on a tall pine tree in the middle of a clearing. At the foot of this tree, a stream of spring water as clear as glass bubbled out of the ground.

할아버지도 도끼를 내려놓고 앉아서 정신나간 사람처럼 그 소리를 들었읍니다. 노래 소리를 들으니까 모든 근심걱정이 사라지는 것 같았읍니다. 할아버지는 그 작은 새의 아름다운 노래 소리에 아무 생각도 나지 않았읍니다.

갑자기 새가 산 위쪽에 있는 다른 나무로 후르룩 날아가 버렸읍니다. 그리고는 거기서 다시 그 황홀한 노래를 부르기 시작했읍니다. 할아버지는 일어나서 새소리가 나는 곳으로 걸어갔읍니다.

할아버지가 가까이 다가가자 새는 좀더 먼 나뭇가지로 후르룩 날아가서 앉았읍니다. 할아버지는 어떤 일이 있어도 그 새를 놓치고 싶지 않아 다시 부지런히 뒤쫓아 갔읍니다.

이렇게 하여 새는 할아버지를 점점더 깊은 숲 속으로 끌고 갔읍니다. 마침내 새는 어느 빈 터의 한가운데 서 있는 커다란 소나무 위에서 쉬었읍니다. 소나무의 밑둥치 쪽에는 유리보다도 맑은 샘물 줄기가 땅에서 졸졸 솟아 오르고 있었읍니다.

7

The old man had been chopping wood and walking through the forest all morning, and the sight of the sparkling water made him feel very thirsty indeed.

He scooped up the water with his hands and drank. It was the sweetest, freshest water he had ever tasted. He bent down and drank until his thirst was satisfied.

Then a very strange thing happened. The old man felt his whole body tingling, and all the aches and pains in his back vanished as if they had never been there. He lay down on a large flat rock above the spring, singing a happy tune to himself. Soon he was fast asleep.

　할아버지는 나무를 찍고 또 오전 내내 숲속을 헤매었기 때문에 반짝거리는 물을 보자 몹시 목이 말랐읍니다.

　할아버지는 손바닥으로 물을 퍼마셨읍니다. 여태까지 마셔봤던 물 중에서 가장 달콤하고 산뜻한 물이었읍니다. 할아버지는 허리를 구부리고 갈증이 가실 때까지 물을 마셨읍니다.

　그런데 아주 이상한 일이 일어났읍니다. 할아버지의 온몸이 얼얼해지면서 쑤시고 아프던 등어리가 아무렇지도 않았던 것처럼 말끔해졌읍니다. 할아버지는 샘 윗쪽에 있는 크고 편편한 바위에 드러누워 즐거운 노래를 불렀읍니다. 그러다가 곧 깊이 잠들어 버렸읍니다.

When the old man woke up, the whole afternoon had already flown by and night was swiftly falling. There was no sign of the little bird, or the sound of its beautiful song. He got up and went down to fetch the wood he had chopped that morning.

"That's very strange," he thought as he carried the wood back home. "Why do I feel so different?" The load on his back felt so light that he looked behind him to make sure it was still there. Even his body felt lighter than air. He wanted to skip down the path just as he used to many years before.

Meanwhile the old man's wife was at home worrying herself sick. It was already dark outside and her husband still hadn't come. Finally she went over to the mean old farmer's house to ask for help.

"Well, it's too late to go out looking for him now," the farmer replied, "and anyway, the tigers have probably eaten him up already."

The old woman was very upset by the farmer's heartless words. She went back to her house to fetch a lantern, and was just about to go up the mountain in search of her husband when he suddenly appeared at the door.

"What's the matter with you?" the old man asked his wife as he stepped inside. She was staring at him with her mouth open.

"Is that really you?" she stammered.

"Well, who else could I be?" the old man laughed.

"Good heavens," she cried, "what's happened to you? You look just like you were on the day of our marriage!"

The old man rushed over to the mirror and gasped. Sure enough, his crooked back had become straight as a board, and all the wrinkles on his face had disappeared. His wife was right. He had become a young man all over again.

"What on earth did you do on the mountain yesterday?" asked his wife.

The old man told her all about the little bird and the mysterious spring water.

"My goodness," cried his wife, "the bird must have led you to a magic spring!" Then she thought for a moment and said, "I should drink some of that water, too. Why, you've become a handsome young man, and I'm still an old hag. The neighbors will laugh if they see us together."

할아버지가 잠에서 깼을 때는 이미 오후 시간은 지나가 버리고 곧 밤이 다가오고 있었 읍니다. 작은 새와 그 아름다운 노래소리는 온데 간데 없어졌읍니다. 할아버지는 일어 나서 아침에 잘라 두었던 나무들을 가지러 내려갔읍니다.

"그것 참 이상하다." 할아버지는 나무를 지고 집으로 돌아오면서 혼자 생각했읍니다. "내가 왜 이렇게 다른 사람처럼 느껴지지?" 등에 지고 있는 나뭇짐이 너무 가볍게 느 껴져서 할아버지는 그 짐이 없어지지 않았는지 보려고 뒤돌아 보았읍니다. 몸은 바람보 다 더 가벼워진 것 같았읍니다 할아버지는 여러해 전처럼 껑충껑충 뛰어가고 싶었읍니다.

한편 집에 있던 할머니는 애태우며 걱정을 하고 있었읍니다. 밖은 이미 어두워졌는 데도 할아버지는 돌아오지 않았읍니다. 마침내 할머니는 근처에 사는 심술장이 할아버 지에게 도움을 청하러 갔읍니다.

"글쎄요. 지금은 너무 늦어서 그 친구를 찾으러 갈 수가 없겠는데요." 농부가 말했읍 니다. "어쩌면 이미 호랑이들에게 잡아 먹혀 버렸을지도 몰라요."

할머니는 그 농부의 무정한 말에 몹시 화가 났읍니다. 할머니는 등불을 가지러 집으 로 돌아왔읍니다. 그리고는 남편을 찾아 산으로 올라가려고 나서는데 갑자기 할아버지 가 문앞에 나타났읍니다.

"여보, 무슨 일이 있었소?" 할아버지가 문안으로 들어서면서 할머니에게 물었읍니다. 할머니는 입을 딱 벌린 채 할아버지를 쳐다보았읍니다.

"정말 당신이에요?" 할머니가 더듬거리며 물었읍니다.

"그럼, 내가 누구란 말이오?" 할아버지가 웃었읍니다.

"맙소사," 할머니가 외쳤읍니다. "대관절 어떻게 된 일이에요? 당신은 지금 마치 우 리가 결혼했을 때처럼 젊어 보이잖아요!"

할아버지는 얼른 거울 있는 데로 뛰어가서는 그만 깜짝 놀랐읍니다. 정말 그의 구부 러진 등은 판자처럼 쭉 펴졌고, 얼굴에 있던 주름살은 모두 싹 없어졌읍니다. 아내의 말이 맞았읍니다. 그는 완전히 다시 젊은이가 되었읍니다.

"당신 어제 산에서 도대체 무엇을 했어요?" 아내가 물었읍니다.

할아버지는 할머니에게 작은 새와 이상한 샘물 이야기를 하나도 빼지 않고 했읍니다.

"맙소사," 할머니가 외쳤읍니다. "그 새가 당신을 요술의 샘으로 인도했군요." 그 리고는 잠시 생각에 잠겼다가 말했읍니다. "나도 그 샘물을 좀 마셔야겠어요. 당신은 멋있는 젊은이가 되었는데 나는 아직도 늙은 할멈이잖아요. 이웃 사람들이 우리를 보면 웃을거예요."

So the next day, her husband took her to the magic spring. Then she drank a few mouthfuls of the mysterious water, and in no time at all she had become a young woman again.

From that day on, the two of them were as happy as can be. They did twice as much work as they used to without feeling tired at all, and so they earned enough to have a nice comfortable life.

It wasn't long before the rumor got around, and soon the greedy farmer was at the door, begging them to tell him where the magic spring was. As soon as they had told him, he was out the door in the blink of an eye.

그래서 다음날 남편이 아내를 요술샘으로 데리고 갔읍니다. 할머니는 그 신기한 물을 몇 모금 마셨읍니다. 그러자 금방 다시 젊은 여자로 바뀌었읍니다.

그날부터 두 사람은 아주 행복하게 살아갔읍니다. 그들은 옛날처럼 피곤함을 전연 모르고 갑절로 많은 일을 했읍니다. 그리고 편안하고 넉넉하게 살아갈 수 있을 만큼 돈도 벌었읍니다.

이 소문은 금방 이웃에 퍼졌고, 그 욕심장이 농부가 찾아와서 요술의 샘이 어디 있는지 가르쳐 달라고 졸라댔읍니다. 그 젊은 부부가 말을 마치자마자, 농부는 눈깜짝할 사이에 문밖으로 뛰어나갔읍니다.

But when morning came the farmer still hadn't come back, and the young couple began to worry. Finally, they went up the mountain to look for him. Curiously enough, when they got to the magic spring there was no sign of the farmer. Instead, they could hear the sound of a baby crying.

"That's strange," said the young woman. "What's a baby doing out here in the mountains? Let's go and have a look."

The young couple climbed onto the large flat rock by the spring. Then they gasped with astonishment. There, on the rock, lay a tiny baby wrapped up in the farmer's clothes.

"Well, well," said the young man, "the farmer overdid it this time."

"What do you mean?" asked his wife. "The farmer?"

14

　그런데 아침이 되도록 그 농부가 돌아오지 않자 젊은 부부는 걱정을 하기 시작했읍니다. 마침내 그들은 농부를 찾으러 산으로 갔읍니다. 이상하게도 젊은 부부가 요술의 샘에 와보니 농부는 그림자도 안보였읍니다. 그 대신에 어린 아기의 울음소리만 들렸읍니다.

　"그것 참 이상한데." 젊은 부인이 말했읍니다. "어린 아기가 이 산속에서 무얼 하고 있는 걸까? 우리 가서 한번 살펴봐요."

　젊은 부부는 샘 옆에 있는 크고 편편한 바위 위로 올라갔읍니다. 그리고는 깜짝 놀라 숨도 제대로 쉬지 못했읍니다. 바로 그 바위 위에 그 농부의 옷을 걸친 갓난 아이가 누워 있었읍니다.

　"저런, 저런." 젊은 남자가 말했읍니다. "그 농부가 이번에도 욕심을 부렸군."

　"무슨 뜻이에요?" 아내가 물었읍니다. "농부라니요?"

"Yes, can't you see?" said the young man. "The farmer drank too much magic spring water. He drank and drank, and became younger and younger. In the end he drank so much spring water that he turned into a baby again."

The young couple couldn't help laughing. In fact, they laughed and laughed until they were out of breath.

"All these years we had no children," said the young woman thoughtfully. "This poor baby has no parents. Why don't we take care of him?"

So the greedy farmer grew up again in the house of the kind young couple. He made his new parents very happy, and under their care he became a gentle, hard-working farmer who never cheated anybody.

"그래요. 모르겠소?" 남자가 말했습니다. "그 농부가 요술의 샘물을 너무 많이 마신거요. 물을 자꾸 마시니까 젊어지고 또 젊어진 것이요. 마침내 샘물을 너무 많이 마셨기 때문에 다시 애기가 되어버린 것이라오."

젊은 부부는 웃지 않을 수 없었습니다. 사실 그들은 웃고 또 웃어서 숨이 다 막힐 지경이었습니다.

"우리에겐 그 동안 어린애가 없었어요." 젊은 여자가 조심스럽게 말했습니다. "이 불쌍한 애기에게도 부모가 없잖아요. 우리가 데려다 키우는 게 어때요?"

그래서 그 욕심장이 농부는 친절한 젊은 부부네 집에서 다시 자라났습니다. 애기는 새로 맞은 부모들을 대단히 행복하게 했으며, 부모님 슬하에서 남을 속이지도 않고, 착하고 부지런히 일하는 농부가 되었습니다.

Three-Year Hill

Not so long ago, there lived an old man who used to believe all sorts of strange things.

One fine day this old man was walking back home from the market. Between the market and his house stood a large hill, and every day many villagers would cross over this hill on their way to market and back.

The old man was walking down the hill on his way home enjoying the beautiful view. In fact, he was so busy enjoying the view that he didn't look where he was going, and suddenly he tripped over a stone and fell flat on his face. Luckily, he didn't hurt himself too much except for a few bruises. But strangely enough, instead of getting up, the old man just sat there in the middle of the road looking very miserable indeed.

3년 고개

그리 오래지 않은 옛날, 온갖 이상한 일들
을 다 믿는 한 할아버지가 살고 있었읍니다.

어느 화창한 날 이 할아버지가 장에 갔다
집으로 돌아오는 길이었읍니다. 장과 할아버
지의 집 사이에는 큰 고개가 하나 있었는데,
마을 사람들은 모두 날마다 이 고개를 지나
장에 갔다오곤 했읍니다.

할아버지는 아름다운 경치를 즐기면서 집
을 향해 고갯길을 내려오고 있었읍니다. 사
실은 경치를 구경하는 데 정신이 팔려 앞을
보지도 않고 걷다가, 갑자기 돌에 걸려 앞
으로 꼬꾸라졌읍니다. 다행히 몇 군데 멍이
들었을 뿐 크게 다친 데는 없었읍니다. 그
런데도 이상한 일은 그 할아버지가 일어나
지는 않고 길 가운데 그냥 주저 앉아서 아
주 슬픈 표정을 짓는 것이었읍니다.

The reason why the old man felt so sad was that he had heard a strange story about this hill. The villagers called it "Three-Year Hill" because they believed that if anyone fell down while climbing it, they would only live for three more years.

The old man also believed this strange story about Three-Year Hill. So now that he had fallen over, he became extremely worried.

"Why did it happen to me?" he moaned. "You stupid rock, because of you, I can only live for three more years!" He sat there in the middle of the road sobbing and feeling very sorry for himself. Finally he got up and hobbled back to his village.

"Is something wrong with you, dear?" asked the old man's wife when he got back home. "You look as if you've seen a ghost."

그 할아버지가 그렇게 슬퍼한 것은 이 고개에 얽힌 이상한 이야기를 들었기 때문입니다. 마을 사람들은 누구든지 이 고개를 오르내리다 넘어지면 3년 밖에 못 산다고 믿고 있었기 때문에 이 고개를 '3년 고개'라고 불렀읍니다.

이 할아버지도 3년 고개에 관한 이상한 이야기를 믿고 있었읍니다. 이제 그 고개에서 넘어졌으니 큰 걱정이었읍니다.

"왜 하필이면 내가 넘어졌지?" 할아버지는 슬퍼했읍니다. "이 바보같은 돌아, 너 때문에 나는 이제 3년 밖에 못 살잖아!" 할아버지는 길 한가운데 앉아서 흐느끼면서 매우 슬퍼했읍니다. 마침내 할아버지는 일어나서 절름거리며 마을로 돌아왔읍니다.

"무슨 일이라도 있었어요, 여보?" 집에 돌아오자 할머니가 물었읍니다. "당신 귀신한테 홀린 사람같이 보여요."

The old man just stared at the floor without saying anything.

"Did something happen to you at the market?" asked his son anxiously.

The old man took a deep breath and sighed. "What shall I do?" he said. "My days are numbered. I was crossing Three-Year Hill on my way back home, and I tripped over and fell. Now I only have three years left to live."

Then he held his head in his hands and started sobbing and trembling from head to toe.

When his wife and son heard this they also burst into tears. They, too, believed in the mysterious power of Three-Year Hill. But they could think of nothing to say that would console the old man.

22

할아버지는 아무 말도 없이 마루바닥만 내려다 보았읍니다.

"장에서 무슨 일이 있었어요?" 아들이 또 근심스러운 듯이 물었읍니다.

할아버지는 긴 한숨만 내쉴 뿐이었읍니다. "이를 어쩌지?" 할아버지가 말했읍니다. "내가 살 날도 얼마 남지 않았어. 집으로 오는 길에 3년 고개를 넘다가 발을 헛디뎌 넘어지고 말았소. 난 이제 3년 밖에 못 살아."

그리고는 두 손으로 머리를 움켜쥐고는 온몸을 떨면서 흐느꼈읍니다.

이 말을 들은 아내와 아들도 그만 울음을 터뜨렸읍니다. 그들도 역시 그 3년 고개의 괴상한 힘을 믿고 있었읍니다. 그러나 할아버지를 위로해줄 말을 생각해낼 수가 없었읍니다.

23

As the months went by, the old man became more and more anxious. And the more anxious he got, the weaker he became. Soon he lost all his appetite and became seriously ill. His wife couldn't bear to see him in such a state and she tried everything to make him better.

She called a doctor to look at him, and even bought him all kinds of expensive medicines. But the medicine didn't have any effect. All it did was make them poorer. In spite of his wife's devoted efforts, the old man just grew weaker.

The whole family was overcome with sorrow. A rumor went around the village that the old man would soon die because of Three-Year Hill. Then one day, a boy who lived nearby heard the news and came to visit his house.

The boy stepped into the old man's room and bowed very humbly. "There's no reason to worry so much," he said, trying to console the old man. "Before long, you won't have a worry in the world."

달이 갈수록 할아버지는 더욱더 걱정을 했읍니다. 걱정을 하면 할수록 할아버지는 더욱 쇠약해졌읍니다. 곧 그는 식욕을 완전히 잃어버렸고, 심한 병을 앓게 되었읍니다. 그 할머니는 할아버지의 그런 모습을 차마 보고 있을 수가 없어서, 병을 고치려고 온갖 수단을 다 썼읍니다.

할머니는 의원을 부르기도 했고, 값비싼 약도 모두 사들였읍니다. 그러나 약도 소용이 없었읍니다. 이런 일들이 그들을 더욱 가난하게만 만들었읍니다. 부인의 헌신적인 노력에도 불구하고 할아버지는 자꾸만 쇠약해져갔읍니다.

온 가족이 슬픔에 젖었읍니다. 할아버지가 3년 고개 때문에 곧 죽게 되었다는 소문은 온 동네에 퍼졌읍니다. 그러던 어느 날 이웃에 사는 한 소년이 이 소식을 듣고 할아버지의 집으로 찾아왔읍니다.

소년은 할아버지의 방으로 들어서서는 공손하게 절을 했읍니다. "그렇게 걱정하실 필요가 없읍니다." 할아버지를 위로해드리려고 소년은 말했읍니다. "이제 할아버지께서는 조금도 걱정을 안하셔도 될 것입니다."

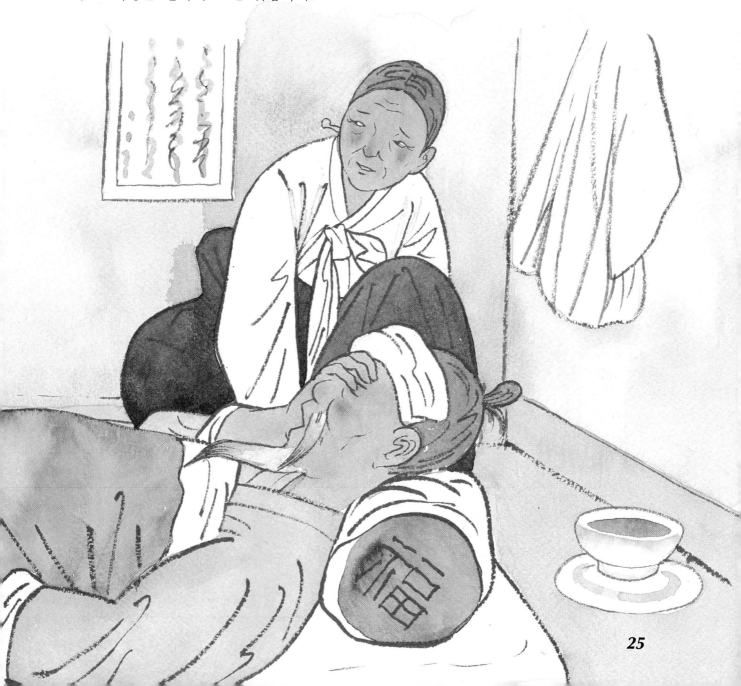

"That's because I'll probably be dead," snapped the old man.

"No, sir, I mean, before long you'll be out of bed and feeling better than ever."

"You must be joking," replied the old man. "Even medicine doesn't do anything for me. I've had it. Don't waste your time on me. I'm going to die whatever you do. Oh, why did I go and fall over on that stupid hill? Why me?" Then the old man started groaning and swaying from side to side.

"There's no need to worry so much about such a little problem," said the boy. "You see, I know a way you can free yourself from the power of Three-Year Hill."

When he heard this, the old man forgot he was sick and sat up with a jerk. "What was that you said?" he asked, his eyes bright with curiosity.

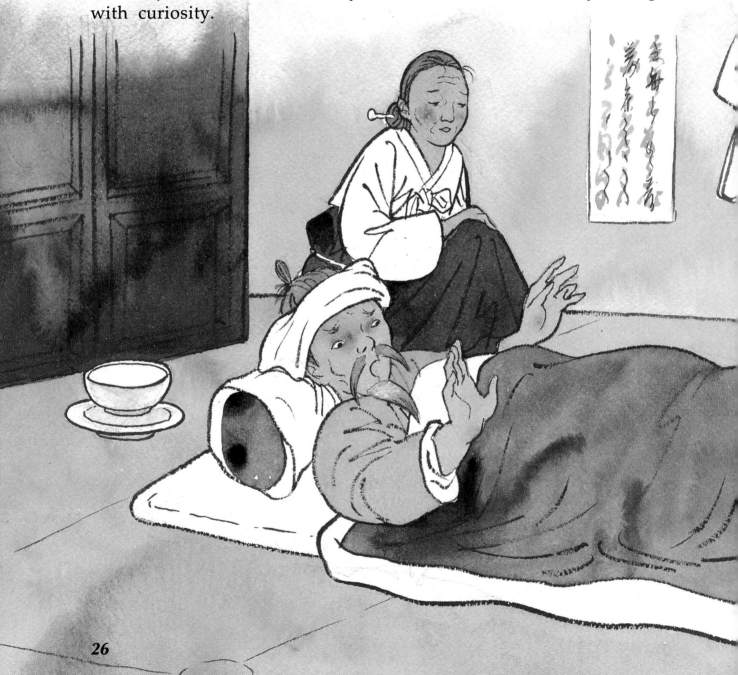

"아마 내가 곧 죽게 될 것이니까 그렇겠지." 할아버지가 말을 가로챘습니다.

"아닙니다. 제 말씀은 할아버지께서 곧 자리에서 일어나셔서 전보다 더 건강해지실 수 있다는 뜻입니다."

"너 지금 농담을 하는게로구나." 할아버지가 대답했습니다. "나에겐 약도 소용이 없어. 이젠 지긋지긋해. 괜히 시간 낭비하지 말아라. 네가 뭐라 하든 나는 죽게될거야. 아, 내가 왜 하필 그 바보같은 고갯길에 올라갔다 넘어졌나? 내가 왜?" 그러면서 할아버지는 신음하며 몸을 뒤척이기 시작했습니다.

"그런 하찮은 일로 그렇게 걱정하실 필요가 없습니다." 소년이 말했습니다. "들어보십시오. 저는 할아버지께서 그 3년 고개의 힘에서 벗어나실 수 있는 방법을 알고 있습니다."

이 말을 듣자 할아버지는 아픈 것도 잊어버리고 벌떡 자리에서 일어나 앉았습니다. "뭐라고 말했지?" 할아버지는 몹시 궁금해 하는 눈빛으로 물었습니다.

"Not only will you free yourself from the power of Three-Year Hill," the boy replied, "but what's more, you'll be able to live much, much longer than anyone else."

"Don't keep me in suspense then," said the old man impatiently. "Tell me about this idea you have."

"Well, all you have to do is go back to the hill and fall over again," answered the boy.

"You cheeky pup," cried the old man, his face turning red. "You came all the way here to play a cruel joke on a poor old man like me?"

"Please let me explain," insisted the boy. "If you fall down once on Three-Year Hill you can only live for three more years, right? So if you fall down twice you can live for six years, if you fall down three times you can live for nine years, four times, twelve years... ha ha ha! Go to Three-Year Hill and fall over as much as you can. The reason why it's called Three-Year Hill is that you live for three more years every time you fall there."

"Now I understand," cried the old man. "I was stupid not to realize that before."

"3년 고개의 힘에서 벗어날 수 있을 뿐만 아니라 그 누구보다도 더 오래 오래 사실 수가 있을 것입니다." 소년이 대답했읍니다.

"그럼 나를 마음 조이게 하지 말아라." 못참겠다는 듯이 할아버지가 말했읍니다. "네가 가지고 있다는 좋은 수를 말해다오."

"그러죠. 할아버지가 그 고개에 다시 가셔서 한 번 더 넘어지시기만 하면 됩니다." 소년이 대답했읍니다.

"예끼 건방진 놈." 얼굴을 붉히면서 할아버지가 고함질렀읍니다. "네가 나같이 불쌍한 노인에게 그런 농담이나 하려고 일부러 여기까지 왔단 말이냐?"

"제 말을 좀 들어보세요." 소년이 우겼읍니다. "할아버지가 3년 고개에서 한 번 넘어지면 3년 밖에 못 사시잖아요. 그렇죠? 그렇다면 할아버지가 두 번 넘어지시면 6년을 사실 수 있잖아요. 그리고 세 번 넘어지시면 9년을 사실 수 있고요. 네 번이면 12년이고요… 하, 하, 하! 3년 고개에 가셔서 넘어질 수 있을 때까지 많이 넘어져 보세요. 3년 고개라고 부르게 된 것도 한 번 넘어질 때마다 3년씩 더 살 수 있기 때문에 붙은 이름이거든요."

"이제야 알겠다." 노인이 외쳤읍니다. "그걸 미처 깨닫지 못하다니 난 참 바보로구나."

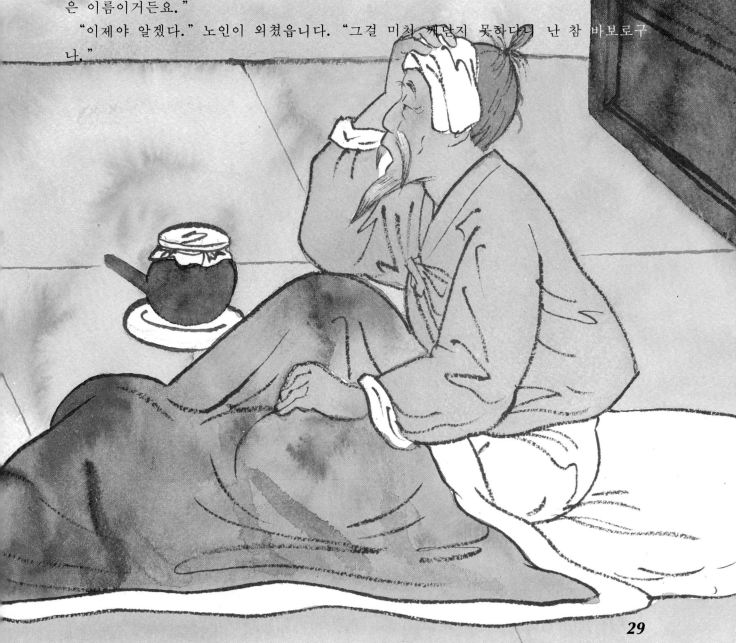

"You see," said the boy. "I told you there was nothing to worry about."

"Yes," replied the old man, "I just didn't think about it. I'll go to Three-Year Hill right now and fall over immediately. Why, I won't only fall over once, I'll roll over and over all the way down the hill."

As soon as he had finished speaking, the old man got up and ran to the hill as fast as his frail legs could carry him. Then he climbed to the top and rolled over and over down the hill saying, "God, please count the number of times I roll down the hill, and let me live many, many years!"

Then he went back to the top and started rolling down again.

Meanwhile the boy, who had been watching from behind a tree, could hardly keep from laughing out loud.

People say that the old man completely recovered his health and lived a very, very long time.

"아셨죠." 소년이 말했읍니다. "제가 아무 걱정할 것 없다고 말씀드렸잖아요."

"옳거니." 노인이 대답했읍니다. "내가 미처 그걸 생각 못했구나. 내 지금 당장 3년 고개로 가서 넘어져야겠다. 물론이고 말고. 한 번만 넘어지진 않을거야. 언덕 아래까지 데굴데굴 굴러내릴거야."

말을 마치자마자 노인은 자리에서 벌떡 일어나 약해진 다리로 있는 힘을 다해 언덕을 향해 뛰어갔읍니다. 그리고는 언덕 꼭대기로 올라가서 데굴데굴 굴러내리면서 말했읍니다. "신령님이시여, 제발 제가 언덕에서 구르는 수를 세셨다가 그만큼 오래오래 살도록 해주십시오!"

그리고는 다시 언덕 꼭대기로 올라가서 또다시 굴러내리기 시작했읍니다.

한편 나무 뒤에 숨어서 이걸 지켜보고 있던 소년은 큰 소리로 웃지 않을 수가 없었읍니다.

노인은 완전히 건강을 되찾았으며 오래오래 살았다고 합니다.

A Word to Parents:

The first story of this volume, *"The Spring of Youth,"* provides an amusing illustration of how too much of a good thing is not necessarily a good thing.

A kind old man earns a meagre living for himself and his wife by chopping wood in the mountains. Everyone in the neighborhood feels sorry that such an old, childless couple must live such a hard life. One morning, while he is chopping wood, the old man is entranced by the song of a little bird perched nearby. The bird leads him deep into the forest and finally comes to rest beside a spring of crystal-clear water. As soon as the thirsty old man drinks from the spring, his whole body starts to tingle and tremble.

When he retrns home his wife can hardly recognize him. They are astonished to discover that he has become a young man all over again. The next day he takes his wife to the spring and she too is mysteriously transformed. The rumor soon gets around, and before long the mean farmer who lives nearby is at the doorstep begging them to tell him where the spring is. When he reaches the spring however, the greedy farmer cannot have enough of the precious water.

He drinks so much that he turns into a helpless little baby. In the end, the old man and his wife adopt him and bring him up to be a gentle hard-working farmer.

The second story, *"Three-Year Hill"* is a hilarious tale of a superstitious old man who finds himself in a tangle. One afternoon, as he walks down the side of a steep hill, he trips on a rock and falls over. This hill is called "Three-Year Hill," as the villagers believe that anyone who stumbles there will only have three years left to live.

This makes the old man so anxious that he becomes seriously ill. Nothing, not even costly medicines and his wife's devoted efforts, seems to make him any better. One day a young man visits his house with some very unusual advice. If falling down once on Three-Year Hill causes one to live for three years, the young man explains, then falling down twice there will cause one to live for six years, three times for nine years, etc.

As soon as he hears this advice, the old man rushes to Three-Year Hill and rolls down it for the rest of the day. People say that he completely recovered his health.

By Mark C. K. Setton

Mark C. K. Setton

Mark C.K. Setton was born in 1952 in Buckinghamshire, England. He graduated from Sungkyunkwan University in 1983 and is presently completing his graduate studies in Oriental Philosophy at the same institution. He has spent the last 10 years in Japan and Korea translating and interpreting for various organizations including UNESCO and the Professors' World Peace Academy of Korea. During that time he has also contributed to various periodicals and newspapers on topics ranging from intercultural exchange to Confucian thought.

Korean Folk Tales Series